Mariam Hoosein

CW00419920

Violin
Grade 3

Pieces
for Trinity College London exams

2016-2019

Published by
Trinity College London
www.trinitycollege.com

Registered in England
Company no. 02683033
Charity no. 1014792

TCL 014832
ISBN 978-0-85736-456-2

9 780857 364562

Show Stopper

Kathy Blackwell (born 1958)
& David Blackwell (born 1961)

Show Stopper by Kathy and David Blackwell from 'Fiddle Time Sprinters'.
© Oxford University Press 2003. Reproduced by permission. All rights reserved.

Allegro Assai

3rd movt from Concertino in D major, op. 15

Ferdinand Küchler
(1867–1937)

Rondinella

George Frideric Handel
(1685–1759)

Do not play the repeats in the exam.

Polonaise

K. 487

Arr. Watson Forbes

Wolfgang Amadeus Mozart
(1756–1791)

Allegretto (♩ = 80)
(spiccato - lower half)

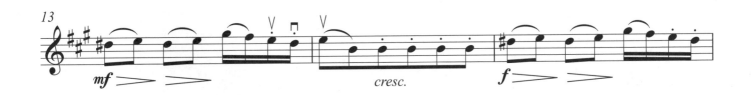

Tambourin

Eleanor Murray & Sebastian Brown

Habanera
from *Carmen*

Arr. K & D Blackwell

Georges Bizet
(1838–1875)

Habanera, from Carmen by Bizet, arranged by Kathy and David Blackwell from 'Fiddle Time Sprinters'.

Beauchamp Rag

Mary Cohen
(born 1954)

London Bridge Variations

Sheila Nelson
(born 1936)

Variation 1: touch the diamond-shaped notes in first position and bow close to the bridge. You will hear the high notes sound as harmonics.

+ = left-hand pizzicato.

© Copyright 1999 by **Guildhall School of Music and Drama**.

The Clowns

Arr. Paul de Keyser

Dmitry Kabalevsky
(1904–1987)

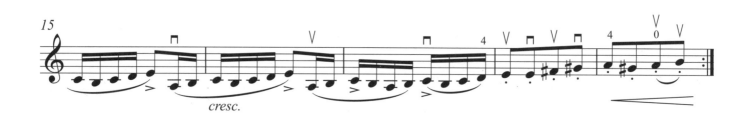

Play the repeat in the exam.

Music by Dmitry Kabalevsky arranged by Paul de Keyser

Ho Down - Show Down

Pamela Wedgwood
(born 1947)

Play the repeats in the exam.

ariam Hoosein

COLLEGE LONDON

Violin
Grade 3

Pieces
for Trinity College London exams

2016-2019

Published by
Trinity College London
www.trinitycollege.com

Registered in England
Company no. 02683033
Charity no. 1014792

Printed in England by Caligraving Ltd.

Show Stopper

Kathy Blackwell (born 1958)
& David Blackwell (born 1961)

Allegro Assai

3rd movt from Concertino in D major, op. 15

Ferdinand Küchler
(1867–1937)

Rondinella

George Frideric Handel
(1685–1759)

Do not play the repeats in the exam.

Polonaise
K. 487

Arr. Watson Forbes

Wolfgang Amadeus Mozart
(1756–1791)

Tambourin

Eleanor Murray & Sebastian Brown

Habanera

from *Carmen*

Arr. K & D Blackwell

Georges Bizet
(1838–1875)

Habanera, from Carmen by Bizet, arranged by Kathy and David Blackwell from 'Fiddle Time Sprinters'.

London Bridge Variations

Sheila Nelson
(born 1936)

Variation 2

The Clowns

Arr. Paul de Keyser

Dmitry Kabalevsky
(1904–1987)

Play the repeat in the exam.

Ho Down - Show Down

Pamela Wedgwood
(born 1947)

Play the repeats in the exam.